# Goodbye, little red hen and other stories

Hannie Truijens

Illustrated by Frances Thatcher

Nelson

# Little red hen is bored

A little red hen sat on her nest.
"I am bored," she said.
"All I do is sit on this nest.
I want to go away, but who will
look after my eggs for me?"

The little red hen went to Mrs Duck.
"Mrs Duck," she said, "I am bored
and I want to go away.
Will you look after my eggs?"
"No," said Mrs Duck, "I am too busy."

The little red hen went to Mrs Goose.
"Mrs Goose," she said, "I am bored
and I want to go away.
Will you look after my eggs?"
"No," said Mrs Goose, "I am
too busy."

The little red hen went back to her nest and sat on her eggs.
"I am still bored," she said.
"Who can look after my eggs for me?"

"Shall I ask Mrs Dove?
No, Mrs Dove is too small.
Shall I ask Mrs Turkey?
No, Mrs Turkey is too big.
Shall I ask Mrs Owl?
No, Mrs Owl will eat my chicks."

6

Crack, crack, crack, went
the eggs.
Out came three little chicks.
"At last," said the little red hen.
She was not bored any more.

"Did you go away, little red hen?"
said Mrs Duck and Mrs Goose.
"No," said the little red hen.
"I was too busy.
I have my three little chicks now."

# Little red hen is clever

The little red hen went for a walk
with her three chicks.
"Don't run away," she said to them.
"The big bad fox will get you."

One little chick saw a bee and
ran away.
The big bad fox got him,
just as the little red hen had said.

"You hide here," said the little red
hen to her two chicks.
"I am going to the fox's den to
get my little chick."

The little red hen went to the
fox's den.
"Come out, you big fat lazy fox,"
she said.
"I can run faster than you."

The fox came out of his den.

"I am not fat," he said.

"AND I am not lazy.

**AND** I can run faster than you."

The fox did run faster than the
little red hen.
But he didn't get her.
"You can run very fast, fox,"
said the little red hen.
"But you can't fly."

The fox went back to his den,
but the little chick had gone.
"That little red hen was too
clever for me," he said.
"Now I have no dinner."

The little red hen walked home with her three chicks.
"Don't ever run away again," she said to them.
And they didn't.

# Goodbye, little red hen

The little red hen was by the river.
Her chicks were big now.
They had all left home.
"Where does this river come from?"
she said.
"And where does it go to?"

Mrs Duck came by.

"Mrs Duck," said the little red hen,

"where does this river come from?"

"I don't know," said Mrs Duck.

"I have never been that far."

Mrs Swan came by.

"Mrs Swan," said the little red hen,

"where does this river go to?"

"I don't know," said Mrs Swan.

"I have never been that far."

Mr Fish put his head out of the
water.
"Mr Fish," said the little red hen,
"where does this river come from?
And where does it go to?"
"I don't know," said Mr Fish.

Mr Water Rat came down the river
in his boat.
"Mr Water Rat," said the little red hen,
"do you know where this river
comes from and where it goes to?"

"Yes," said Mr Water Rat.

"It comes from the hills.

And it goes to the sea."

"Oh," said the little red hen.

"What are hills?

And what is the sea?"

"Come into my boat," said
Mr Water Rat.
"We will go up the river
and I will show you the hills.
Then we will go down the river
and I will show you the sea."

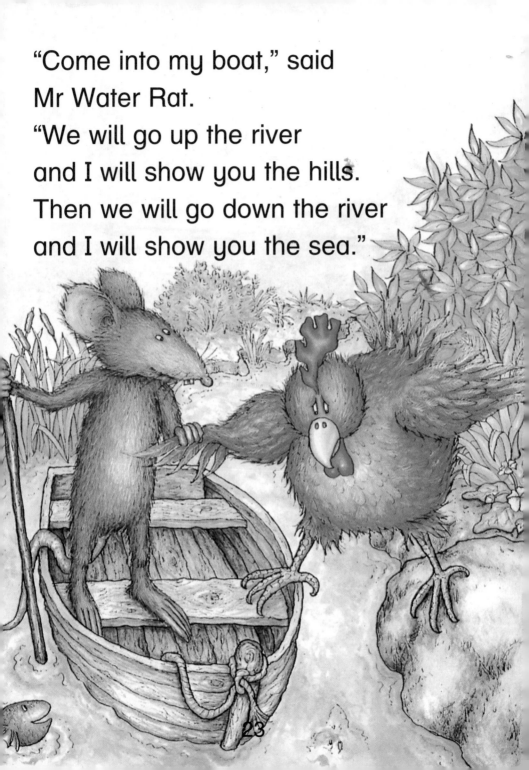

"Goodbye, little red hen.
Goodbye."